★ GRACE IN SPA[CE]

A PICTURE BOOK ABOUT THE HISTORY OF 10 ANIMAL ASTRONAUT HEROES
THROUGH THE EYES OF A COOL CAT

COSMIC ANIMALS LAIKA, MARFUSHA, FRUIT FLIES, ALBERT I, HECTOR THE RAT, HAM THE CHIMPANZEE, FELICETTE, TORTOISES, BULLFROGS, ARABELLA AND ANITA SPIDERS

WRITTEN BY STACY J. SHANEYFELT
ILLUSTRATED BY MARINA MASLOVA

First, I want to give a shout out to my intelligent, funny, and "cool cat" nephew, Preston. Thanks for making me smile!

I also wholeheartedly dedicate this book to the loving memory of my beloved Sooner, a heroic cat who will always race through the space of time in my heart. I pay a special BFF tribute to Lana, for always being a true and loyal friend, even when I'm **SPACEY STACY!**

During a cozy nap on a chilly December day,
Grace, a cool cat, dreams in a celestial way...
Like other animal astronauts before, she yearns to explore.
Headlines fill her purrfect mind, "Grace in Space," and more!

In fact, she'll fight like cats and dogs to achieve this dream.
For added motivation, a galactic book gives her science steam...
Are you ready to read along with Grace and her nine lunar lives?
Let's discover Pet Space Pioneers (PSPs) with our own eyes!

CHAPTER 1:
FAB AND FRUITY FLIERS, 1947

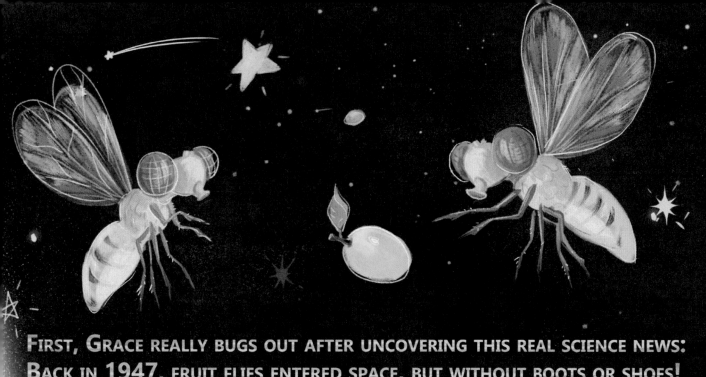

First, Grace really bugs out after uncovering this real science news:
Back in 1947, fruit flies entered space, but without boots or shoes!
Tasked to study radiation at such high heights,
These fab flies on the wall earned the first space right!

CHAPTER 2:
PRIMATE PATHFINDER, ALBERT I, 1948

THEN GRACE GOES BANANAS OVER SOME MONKEY PROOF.
ALBERT I, THE FIRST PRIMATE PATHFINDER, LAUNCHED OVER THE ROOF!
AFTER JETTING IN 1948 FROM NEW MEXICO'S NASA SPACE STATION,
HE LATER INSPIRED THREE MORE FUTURE COUSINS' STARRY EXPLORATIONS!

NEXT, GRACE LEARNS ABOUT A RUSSIAN STRAY DOG.
LAIKA **ZOOMED** INTO SPACE THROUGH CLOUDS AND FOG.
IN **1957**, SHE SHOWED COURAGE IN A COAT.
FOR THAT, THIS DYNAMIC DOG DESERVES MORE THAN A FLOAT!

Chapter 4: A Hopping Historian: Space Bunny, Marfusha, 1959

In addition, Grace bounces like a bunny to continue more. Marfusha's 1959 Russian mission was certainly one to adore!

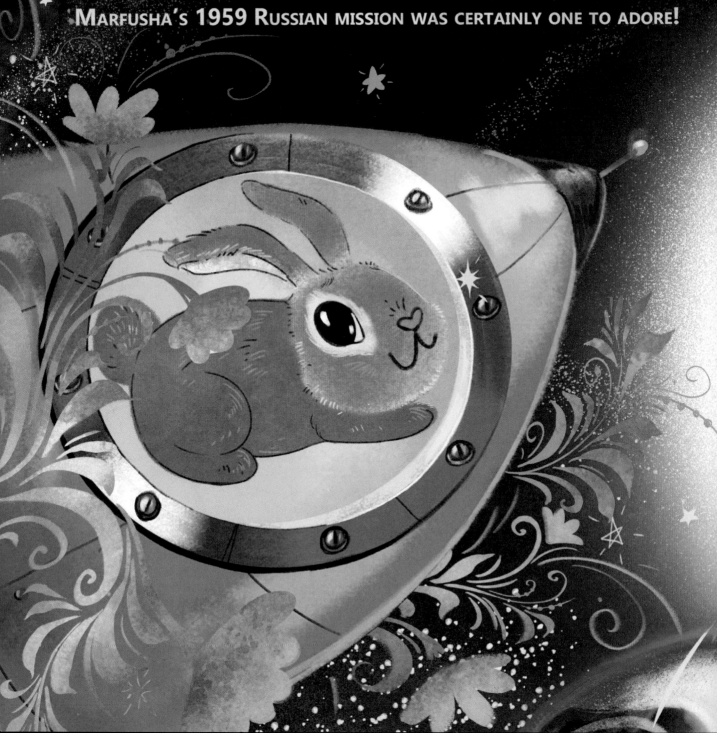

BECAUSE IT'S NEARLY NOON, GRACE CRAVES A SAVORY RODENT SNACK.
YET AFTER SEEING HEROIC HECTOR, SHE CHOOSES CRAB AND CHEESE MAC!
AS THE FIRST SPACE RAT, HECTOR WON THE COSMIC RAT RACE INDEED!
DOES THIS CHANGE GRACE'S MIND ABOUT RODENTS? PLEASE TAKE HEED!

Whether you're a vegetarian, a vegan, or a carnivore as well,
Join giggling Grace and note Ham, the first space chimp, so swell!

CHAPTER 7: FELICETTE, A FAMOUS FRENCH FELINE, 1963

SPECIFICALLY, CHAPTER 7 LETS THE CAT OUT OF THE BAG.
READ ON ALL ANIMAL LOVERS, SO YOU CAN LATER BRAG!

SUDDENLY, GRACE FINDS FELICETTE, A FAMOUS FRENCH FELINE:
AS THE FIRST CAT IN THE COSMOS, SHE WAS STRONG AND FINE!

CHAPTER 8:
SOLAR SHELLS: RUSSIAN TORTOISES, 1968

PRESENTLY CRAVING A MACKEREL MARLENKA, GRACE TURNS TO CHAPTER 8 NOW.
RUSSIAN TORTOISES LAUNCHED IN 1968, WHICH MAKES GRACE MEOW!

CHAPTER 9: JUMPIN' FOR JUPITER: BULLFROGS, 1970

Fast forward to **1970**, when bullfrogs leaped boldly into space. Gathering brain data, they helped the human and animal race!

CHAPTER 10: WEBS OF WONDER: ARABELLA AND ANITA SPIDERS, 1973

SPINNING WITH WEBS OF WONDER, GRACE STUDIES MORE AND MORE.
DID YOU KNOW A SPECIAL SPIDER COUPLE VISITED THE ORBITAL FLOOR?
NAMED ARABELLA AND ANITA, THEY LAUNCHED IN 1973.
BUGGED-EYED WITH ADMIRATION, GRACE IS NOW FILLED WITH GLEE!

FINALLY, ALL **10** ANIMAL HERO CHAPTERS FUEL HER DELIGHTFUL SCIENCE DREAMS.
SHE NOW REALIZES THAT "GRACE IN SPACE," IS TOUGHER THAN IT SEEMS.
PLEASE REMEMBER THAT EVEN MORE ANIMALS WERE SPACE TRAVEL PIONEERS:
GUINEA PIGS, NEWTS, WASPS, AND OTHERS HAVE HELPED HUMANS FOR YEARS!

POST-READING QUESTIONS, DISCUSSIONS, AND FAMILY FUN

1. SPACE CASES:
GO ONLINE WITH YOUR GROWNUP'S PERMISSION AND RESEARCH 4-6 OTHER ANIMALS THAT HAVE ENTERED SPACE. YOU MAY ALSO CHECK OUT A BOOK FROM YOUR LOCAL LIBRARY TO CONNECT WITH SCIENCE, HISTORY, AND GEOGRAPHY!

2. RHYME TIMES:
SCAN THE BOOK AGAIN AND LOCATE 4-6 PAIRS OF RHYMING WORDS FOR READING, SPELLING, WRITING, AND SPEECH PRACTICE.

3. ANIMAL ETHICS:
SKY ROCKET YOUR READING SKILLS NOW AND READ ABOUT HOW NASA TREATS ITS ANIMAL ASTRONAUTS BY AN ONLINE ARTICLE OR FINDING A BOOK ABOUT THIS TOPIC AT YOUR LOCAL LIBRARY

4. ARTFUL ASTRONAUTS:
WHICH PIECE OF ART IS YOUR FAVORITE? WHY? BE ART SMART!

5. SPACE WORDS:
USING CONTEXT CLUES, IDENTIFY 4-6 SPACE WORDS FROM THE STORY AND DEFINE THEM IN YOUR OWN WORDS TO BOOST YOUR VOCABULARY. YOUNGER KIDS WILL ASK AN ADULT TO ASSIST.

6. CONTEMPORARY ART:

USING THE ILLUSTRATOR'S STYLE AS A MODEL,
TRY TO SKETCH, PAINT, COLLAGE, DOODLE, OR COLOR
ANY FEATURED ANIMAL FROM THE BOOK WITH YOUR OWN FLAIR.
CREATE ART FROM THE HEART!

7. VIRTUAL FIELD TRIP:

NAME THREE COUNTRIES REPRESENTED BY THE ANIMAL
ASTRONAUTS. LOCATE THESE 3 NATIONS ON A MAP
OR ATLAS WITH THE HELP OF A GROWNUP.
BE A GEOGRAPHER!

8. MANX MANIA:

FIND 4-6 FUN FACTS ABOUT GRACE'S FELINE BREED BY GOING
ONLINE WITH YOUR PARENTS' PERMISSION OR FINDING A BOOK AT
YOUR LOCAL LIBRARY. MEOW WITH SCIENCE!

9. MATH MAGIC:

SCAN THE BOOK AGAIN AND COUNT THE EXACT NUMBER
OF ANIMALS NAMED. SHOW YOUR MATH MAGIC!

10. SPACE RACE:

DESIGN YOUR OWN MODEL OF WHAT A SPACE RACE
WOULD LOOK LIKE. USE MATERIALS FROM YOUR HOME, BLOCKS, TOYS,
OR ANY SUPPLIES WITH AN ADULT'S PERMISSION. GIVE DIY A TRY!

ABOUT THE AUTHOR

AFTER OBTAINING HER BS IN SECONDARY ENGLISH EDUCATION AND MA IN ENGLISH FROM SLIPPERY ROCK UNIVERSITY OF PA, STACY EMBARKED ON A SUCCESSFUL TEACHING CAREER THAT SPANNED PUBLIC, GOVERNMENT, AND CHARTER SCHOOLS IN PITTSBURGH, PA, OKLAHOMA CITY, NORMAN, OK, AND OKINAWA, JAPAN. SHE PROUDLY EARNED A 2004 FULBRIGHT-HAYS SEMINAR SCHOLARSHIP TO THAILAND AND VIETNAM FROM THE UNITED STATES DEPARTMENT OF EDUCATION, TEACHER OF THE YEAR IN TWO SCHOOLS, AS WELL AS OTHER TEACHING ACCOLADES.

IN ADDITION TO MULTICULTURAL AND SOCIAL ACTIVISM, STACY SAVORS SWEET MOMENTS WITH HER AWESOME HUSBAND, TWO FIERCE AND FABULOUS DAUGHTERS, AND THREE FRISKY FUR BABIES. PRESENTLY WORKING AS A VIRTUAL FREELANCER, SHE GREATLY ENJOYS FILMS, TRAVEL, COFFEE, ART, CATS, BIRD WATCHING, AND ALL THINGS MINDFUL!

ABOUT THE ILLUSTRATOR

ALTHOUGH AN ARCHITECT BY DEGREE, MARINA HAS DEVELOPED HER CAREER AS AN ARTIST SINCE SHE WAS FIVE. A LIFE-LONG PATH AS AN ARTIST HAS TAKEN HER THROUGH DIFFERENT TECHNIQUES AND STYLES. FROM WORKING AS A FREELANCE PORTRAIT ARTIST TO BEING PART OF THE 2D ART TEAM RESPONSIBLE FOR RUSSIAN BLOCKBUSTERS SUCH AS 'SNOW QUEEN 4' AND, MORE RECENTLY, 'SECRET MAGIC CONTROL AGENCY', MARINA HAS ALWAYS HAD HER HEART SET ON ILLUSTRATING STORIES FOR CHILDREN.

NOW THAT SHE HAS BEEN ABLE TO PROVE HERSELF IN THIS PARTICULAR FIELD, SHE WOULD LOVE TO EXPLORE HER CURRENT SKILLS APPLIED TO TRADITIONAL ANIMATION FOR SHORT FILMS. ONE THING IS FOR SURE, SHE IS AVID TO CREATE, ILLUSTRATE AND ANIMATE STORIES THAT INSPIRE, TEACH, AND GIVE JOY TO THE KIDS WHO READ THEM.

THANK YOU FOR BUYING THIS BOOK. AS A WORKING MOM AND MILITARY SPOUSE, YOUR REVIEWS MEAN SO MUCH TO ME BECAUSE I AIM TO UNITE GLOBAL READERS THROUGH ART AND LITERACY. KINDLY POST A SHORT REVIEW ON THIS BOOK'S AMAZON PAGE. I TRULY APPRECIATE YOU FOR BOOK BUZZING WITH ME!

IF YOU LIKE THIS BOOK, THEN PLEASE CHECK OUT MY OTHER BUZZWORTHY OFFERINGS.